The 90-Day
Mindfulness
Journal

10 MINUTES A DAY
to Live in the Moment with Less Stress

S.J. SCOTT & BARRIE DAVENPORT

About
The 90-Day Mindfulness Journal

Mindfulness is a habit that we, as self-improvement authors and bloggers, have wholeheartedly embraced. It has helped both of us become more conscious in our relationships, more grateful and present in our experiences, and more deliberative in our professional endeavors.

Not only do we strive to practice mindfulness in our daily lives, but we are also committed to sharing the benefits of mindfulness practices through our books and journals. We want others around the world to experience the life-altering outcomes that we and millions of other practitioners have discovered through this healing habit.

Our first journal on this topic, *The Mindfulness Journal: Daily Practices, Writing Prompts, and Reflections for Living in the Present Moment* [1], is a 365-day journey with mindfulness that is immersive and comprehensive. It is a great tool for someone who wants to commit to a year-long exploration of mindfulness.

However, after hearing from many of our readers, we learned that some people wanted a more simplified journal practice that could be completed in a shorter number of months and that required ten minutes or less of writing time a day. That's how *The 90-Day Mindfulness Journal* was born.

Whether you are a beginning mindfulness student or a more seasoned practitioner, this journal offers some of the best and most valuable practices, condensed for ease of use and limited time. This journal focuses on three practices that we will explain in further detail in a later section. These practices include:

1. Mindful awareness of your thoughts and emotions.
2. Mindfulness in your daily activities.
3. A mindfulness meditation practice.

With these three endeavors, you'll strengthen your practice so that mindfulness becomes a regular habit with just ten minutes of daily writing, and you will have completed enough mindfulness-related activities to experience many of the mental, physical, and emotional benefits.

We are especially mindful (and grateful) that you have made the choice to purchase this journal and begin this 90-day adventure with us. Thank you for your trust in our work.

It is our sincere hope that you find this experience to be rewarding and even life-changing.

Mindfully yours,

Barrie Davenport & Steve "S.J." Scott

Mindfulness:
How to *Truly* Live in the Present Moment.

You might wonder if mindfulness is the latest fad, like the "Pet Rock" or the Atkins Diet. You see it everywhere—in books, blog posts, magazines, news programs, and smartphone apps.

It has even crept into the products we buy, like mindfulness coloring books, meditation cushions, and affirmation CDs.

What is all the hoopla about? Why is mindfulness suddenly on the minds of so many? And will it fade into obscurity like so many other trends have in the past?

If you're new to mindfulness and have been skeptical about whether or not it has any useful application in your life—we'd like to assure you of its longevity and life-changing value.

The practice of mindfulness is not new, and it's certainly not a fad. People around the world have been practicing mindfulness for thousands of years, whether by itself or as part of a larger tradition.

It has been part of various religious and secular practices, including Hinduism, Buddhism, yoga and, more recently, non-religious mindfulness meditation.

It also has roots in Judaism, Christianity, and Islam, although most modern Western practitioners and teachers of mindfulness learned about it in the Buddhist and Hindu traditions.

Today, mindfulness is used regularly in the field of positive psychology. It was popularized in Western culture by Jon Kabat-Zinn, a molecular biologist and meditator who created mindfulness-based stress reduction (MBSR) in the 1970s to treat patients struggling with life challenges and physical or mental illness.

Both MBSR and mindfulness-based cognitive therapy (MBCT) are valued and accepted tools for psychologists to use in treating patients around the world.

Mindfulness meditation is not only used in clinical settings, but also in the military, in schools, and even in large corporations. It's a widely implemented educational practice in a variety of settings, and has become a go-to tool for anyone who wants to reduce stress and increase well-being.

So is mindfulness here to stay?

It has become increasingly mainstream in recent years, and

more and more individuals are adopting the practice as part of their regular self-care routines. As people discover the remarkable benefits of a mindfulness practice, it will become an established and essential tool for our health and well-being—just like exercise and a healthy diet.

That's why we have created *The 90-Day Mindfulness Journal*. We want to help you enjoy the benefits of mindfulness by offering a practical tool to help you create *the habit* of mindfulness in daily life.

With this journal, you will cement the practice of being mindful during the next 90 days, and you'll engage in specific mindfulness activities that will change your life for the better.

Are you new to mindfulness? If so, take a moment to read the next section so you have a better idea of what mindfulness is.

What

Exactly Is Mindfulness?

If you don't have a regular mindfulness practice now, you might be unsure about what mindfulness really is. Is it meditation? Is it a religion? Is it an exercise?

Mindfulness is really simple:

It is intentional awareness of the present moment.

Whatever you are doing, thinking, or observing, that's where your attention flows. You are here, now. Not dwelling in the past. Not worrying about the future.

You can practice mindfulness while:

- Taking a walk
- Eating a meal
- Brushing your teeth
- Drinking your tea
- Meditating
- Washing the dishes
- Breathing
- Journaling
- Engaging in any activity that requires your attention and

focus on the task at hand

In addition to present moment awareness, mindfulness also involves the practice of non-judgment. Non-judgment means you observe your experiences, thoughts, and feelings without labeling them as good or bad, right or wrong.

This detachment from judging the moment—and simply experiencing it—removes the filter of appraisal that distracts you from the actual experience.

Our brains quickly assess things as good or bad, useful or not useful, and so on. Because of our need to judge, our moments are often tainted by our thoughts about them before we can fully process the experiences.

With *non-judgmental awareness*, your mindfulness practice no longer has these filters, allowing you to fully and authentically experience the moment.

Judgments about our thoughts, experiences, and interactions can also cause us needless suffering and anxiety, especially when we have negative and self-defeating thoughts.

When we attach to these thoughts and view them as true, they begin to define our reality. Often, our thoughts have little to do with reality, yet they can still make us anxious, angry, or depressed. Avoiding the suffering these thoughts cause is another compelling reason to practice non-judgment.

So to sum it up, you can define mindfulness in an easy-to-remember manner:

Present Moment Awareness

+

Non-Judgment of Thoughts, Feelings, and Experiences

=

Mindfulness

Understanding the concept of mindfulness is easy. The hard part is putting it into practice. Staying present is more difficult than it might seem because your mind tends to dance around like a wild monkey.

As soon as you try to tame your mind to focus on the moment, it careens off in different directions, hopping wildly from thought to thought. These thoughts are frequently negative and distracting, pulling you away from the moment and into a rabbit hole of worry or regret.

But you can tame your "monkey mind" with practice. The

more you practice mindfulness in daily life, the more control you have over your thoughts and where you want to focus them.

Some mindfulness practices, like mindfulness meditation, can accelerate your ability to be more mindful in your daily life. With meditation, you intentionally train your mind by focusing on your breathing and calming your thoughts by allowing them to float in and out of your mind without attaching to them.

Meditation strengthens your "mind muscle" and allows you to return to the present moment more quickly and without as much mental interference from unwanted thoughts.

There are many other intentional mindfulness practices (like yoga, repeating affirmations, guided imagery, and mindfulness journaling, such as you are doing here) that will also strengthen your mental muscle, so you can more easily apply mindfulness to your basic daily activities.

You might wonder why you need to apply mindfulness in everyday life. Let's look at its benefits and how using *this* journal can improve your mental, physical, and emotional well-being.

10 Health Benefits
of Mindfulness

One of the reasons mindfulness is getting so much attention is the research that continues to come out about it. Study after study [2] confirms that mindfulness practices have a myriad of physical, mental, and emotional benefits.

In our book, *10-Minute Mindfulness*, we outline in detail these benefits and the scientific research supporting them. But here is a brief overview of what you can expect from practicing mindfulness:

#1. Mindfulness reduces rumination and overthinking.

Rumination is a maladaptive form of self-reflection that has an addictive quality. When you're constantly "in your head," looping negative thoughts, brooding, and thinking about the past, you put yourself at a much greater risk for mental health problems like depression and anxiety.

Research studies suggest that practicing mindfulness helps reduce rumination. In a study by Chambers, et al. [3], participants (with no previous meditation experience) in a mindfulness meditation retreat reported significantly higher mindfulness, less rumination, and fewer symptoms of depression than the control group.

#2. Mindfulness alleviates some stress.
A mindfulness practice can decrease the levels of the stress hormone cortisol, according to the results of the Chambers, et al. study (as well as numerous other studies). The study shows a direct connection between resting cortisol and scores on a mindfulness scale.

#3. Mindfulness improves memory, concentration, and performance.
Mindfulness practices have been shown to improve focus, memory, and reading comprehension, as well as reducing mind-wandering. Students who practice mindfulness [4] perform better on tests than those who don't.

Researchers at Massachusetts General Hospital [5] revealed in a study that regular meditation causes the brain's cerebral cortex to thicken. The cerebral cortex is responsible for higher brain functions like memory, concentration, and learning.

#4. Mindfulness helps with emotional reactivity.
Daily stressors in our lives impact our ability to maintain emotional stability so we don't react with anger and emotional

outbursts. Mindfulness helps us respond to stressful situations in calmer, healthier ways.

A study by Ortner, et al. [6] showed that mindfulness meditation allowed participants to disengage from emotionally upsetting pictures and focus better on cognitive tasks, as compared with people who saw the pictures but did not practice mindfulness meditation.

#5. Mindfulness promotes cognitive flexibility.
Cognitive flexibility is the ability to change your train of thought quickly to adapt to the demands of the situation. A 2009 study [7] revealed that the practice of mindfulness meditation promotes cognitive flexibility and helps our thinking to be less rigid and more creative.

#6. Mindfulness creates happier relationships.
A University of North Carolina study [8] of "relative happy, non-distressed couples" found that the couples who actively practiced mindfulness saw improvements in their relationship happiness. They experienced less stress in their relationships and were able to cope with challenges more easily.

#7. Mindfulness reduces anxiety.
Mindfulness practices help shrink the amygdala [9]—the fear

center of the brain. The practices increase the prefrontal cortex to promote a calmer, steadier brain. The practice of detachment and non-judgment of anxious thoughts and feelings helps lessen fearful reactivity to the thoughts.

#8. Mindfulness improves sleep.

Insomnia and sleep problems are common stress reactions. Mindfulness habits promote calm and reduce rumination that can disrupt sleep.

A 2015 study [10] of older adults confirms that mindfulness meditation practices support getting a better night's sleep. According to the study, mindfulness meditation can "increase the relaxation response through its function of increasing attentional factors that impart control over the autonomic nervous system."

#9. Mindfulness promotes mental health.

University of Oregon researchers [11] found that a mindfulness technique called "integrative body-mind training" can result in brain changes that may be protective against mental illness. The practice of the technique "induces positive structural changes in brain connectivity by boosting efficiency in a part of the brain that helps a person regulate behavior," according to the study.

#10. Mindfulness provides pain relief.

A variety of studies [12] support the findings that mindfulness practices help people relieve and cope with chronic pain. Mindfulness helps people notice pain without judgment, as negative thoughts and judgments exacerbate pain.

These practices also afford a more accurate perception of pain, reducing the secondary suffering that comes with evaluating and worrying about pain. Researchers have seen a reduction in pain intensity and a lessening of pain unpleasantness with participants who practiced mindfulness meditation.

As you practice mindfulness, you create changes in your brain function and structure that reinforce these benefits. Just as exercise habits will change your body, mindfulness habits will literally reshape your mind.

In addition to the benefits listed above, mindfulness expands your sense of time as you become less distracted by the demands of daily life. When you are focused on the task or experience at hand with full attention, you slow down and savor it.

Your mind isn't racing ahead to the next thing you need to do. You have a more profound and immersive experience of any activity or interaction that leads to a deep level of awareness.

Mindfulness also heightens your feelings of gratitude and appreciation. When you focus your full attention on the moment, you can see the beauty in it. Even the most mundane tasks become more pleasurable because you recognize how fleeting and precious they are.

Modern life, with all of its distractions and demands, has made it increasingly difficult to rest in the here and now. Mindfulness is the secret to reclaiming your life on your own terms and cherishing every moment of it.

The Mindfulness Benefits
of Journaling

Writing in a journal gives you a double dose of mindfulness. You are tethered to the present moment both by the physical act of writing and the mindfulness activity you are writing about.

As you journal, your mind is fully engaged with the action of pen moving across paper. Writing by hand (rather than typing) requires that your brain slows down to better organize your thoughts and consider the big picture or a different perspective.

In the flow of journaling, there is little space for thoughts about past regrets and future worries. You, your mind, and your pen and paper become one in the here and now. This flow state occurs regardless of what you are journaling about, as long as you are absorbed in the process and find it pleasurable or cathartic.

In fact, the process of journaling shares many of the science-backed benefits of mindfulness. Studies have shown that journaling:

- Relieves stress and helps you cope with traumatic events.
- Is highly effective in helping people manage symptoms of depression.
- Helps you manage anxiety symptoms.
- Promotes self-reflection and self-awareness.
- Improves your overall health and well-being.
- Reduces blood pressure and boosts the immune system.
- Improves physical and psychological health for cardiac patients.
- Improves your sleep.

(If you'd like to learn more about the benefits of journaling, check out our book *Effortless Journaling: How to Start a Journal, Make It a Habit, and Find Endless Writing Topics* [13].)

Also, when you are journaling, you create something that isn't a final product that you must judge or evaluate. In fact, it is essential that you avoid judging your journaling efforts if you want to enjoy the full mindfulness benefits of the practice. The process of journaling is the goal—not what you write or how well you write it.

Being fully present as you journal strengthens the creative flow of writing *and* your ability to be present. Writing down your feelings, thoughts, and observations helps you notice and pay closer attention to both your inner and outer worlds.

When was the last time you really focused on the starkness of tree branches on a winter day, or the subtle sound of wind rustling the leaves? How much thought have you given to the feeling of water running over your hands as you rinse out your coffee cup? How often do you notice the way your thoughts impact your feelings?

Journaling is a mindfulness practice that encourages you to pay attention *with intention and purpose.*

As we say in *Effortless Journaling,* "When you willingly and actively come to your journal to write, you pause and carve out the time to explore your feelings and observations in a deeper and more compelling way."

Now that you know *how* mindfulness journaling can help you, let's go over a simple process for building the habit. Then we'll talk about how to maximize the benefit from this journal.

How to Build
the Mindfulness Journaling Habit

It's not hard to create the mindfulness journaling habit. All you have to do is schedule this activity and use simple habit-building strategies to make sure you never miss a day.

Both authors (Steve "S.J." Scott & Barrie Davenport) talk extensively about creating habits on their websites, but for now, here's an overview of the simple, seven-step process.

Step #1: Focus on Building Just the Mindfulness Habit

One common mistake is trying to build multiple habits at the same time. This problem relates to **"ego depletion,"** which is a person's "diminished capacity to regulate their thoughts, feelings, and actions," according to the book *Willpower* by Roy F. Baumeister and John Tierney.

Our willpower is like a muscle. It weakens throughout the day because of constant use. You use your willpower when you make dozens of decisions each day. You use your willpower to concentrate at work. You use it to resist eating junk food. And you use it to resist lashing out at others when you're tired from a long day of work.

Because of ego depletion, your ability to form new habits is limited since there are only so many "new" things your will-power can handle at once. To keep things easy, we <u>strongly recommend</u> that you work on building *just* the mindfulness practice for the next month, increasing the likelihood that you'll make this habit stick!

Step #2: Commit to 30 (or More) Days of Mindfulness

Mindfulness will help you gain a new appreciation for life. But this doesn't mean it will be a simple or quick process. In fact, it might take you a few attempts to turn journaling into a permanent behavior.

Some people say it takes 21 days to build a habit, while others claim it takes up to 66 days. The truth is that the length of time varies from person to person and from habit to habit. You'll find that some habits are easy to build, while others require more effort. Our advice is to commit to being mindful for a *minimum* of the next 30 days.

We recommend that you schedule a daily block of at least five to ten minutes to write in this journal.

Step #3: Anchor Mindfulness to an Established Habit

Practicing mindfulness *shouldn't* be based upon motivation, fads, or temporary desire. Rather, it should be integrated in your life in a way that allows the behavior to become automatic. To do this, you don't need a series of sophisticated steps—just a simple strategy you can commit to, day in and day out, without fail.

We suggest that you "anchor" the journaling practice to habits that you *already* do daily. These habits should be automatic on your part—like eating, sleeping, or going to the bathroom. You wouldn't forget to complete any of these actions, so by attaching your mindfulness habit to one of them, you won't forget to perform it either.

When anchoring, your goal is to practice mindfulness before or after you complete one of these habits:

- Drinking your first cup of tea (or coffee) in the morning.
- When your alarm clock goes off.
- When you get into bed in the evening (you can also create a visual cue by leaving this journal on your night-stand).

- Before or after you finish a specific meal (breakfast, lunch, or dinner).
- When you walk into a specific room for the first time (e.g., your den or home office).

There are countless options for picking an established habit. The trick is to identify an action you do every single day and attach mindfulness journaling to it. When you pick the *right* habit, you'll discover that it's not hard to turn mindfulness into an automatic behaviour.

Step #4: Track the Mindfulness Habit

It's not enough to anchor mindfulness to another habit—you also need a mechanism to reinforce this behavior daily.

The simplest tool for building reinforcement is your mobile phone (since it's a device most people have on them through-out the day). We suggest that you install one of three apps, and use it to create reminders for practicing the mindfulness habit.

- **Strides (http://www.stridesapp.com)**: Strides has a clean, simple interface that allows you to track all your habits and goals.
- **Coach.me (https://www.coach.me)**: This is another

great tool. Not only can you use it to stick to your habits, you can also connect with a coach to help you build a specific habit.

- **Chains (https://chains.cc)**: Chains is built on Jerry Seinfeld's "never break the chain" concept [14], where you commit to a specific habit and never miss a day, creating a chain of positive behavior in your life.

Finally, if you're not interested in downloading a whole new app, you can also set a reminder to practice mindfulness using one of these productivity tools:

- Google Calendar (https://calendar.google.com)
- Evernote (https://evernote.com)
- Todoist (https://todoist.com)

Regardless of the tool you pick, we recommend keeping track of your journaling habit by using some type of tool. You'll be surprised at how often the behavior of "checking in" makes the difference between whether you do or do not practice mindfulness for the day

Step #5: Plan for Potential Obstacles

With any new habit, you'll face obstacles—even mindfulness journaling. While this practice might seem simple to complete, there *will* be those days when it seems impossible to carve out an extra five to ten minutes.

You'll probably encounter obstacles like:

- Not having enough time.
- Feeling too self-conscious with certain prompts.
- Forgetting to pack *The 90-Day Mindfulness Journal* for a vacation.
- Feeling too angry (or sad, upset, stressed, etc.) to practice mindfulness.
- Struggling to think of unique ways to live in the present moment.

The key to overcoming (or even preventing) these obstacles is recognizing that they happen to all of us. Once you do, you can create a specific plan for how you'll handle each of the challenges that you frequently experience.

We recommend you create "if-then statements" for the actions you'll take when certain challenges arise.

Here are a few examples:
- "If I keep forgetting to practice mindfulness, then I will schedule this habit for earlier in the day when I have more time."

- "If I can't think of any reason to be mindful, then I'll write down ideas as they come to me throughout the day."
- "If I have a bad day and don't feel in the mood to journal, then I will simply focus on trying to find just one positive thing to write about."
- "If I forget my journal, then I will keep a list of mindfulness exercises on my cell phone, and update the journal when it's available."
- "If I find myself stressed or angry at the world, then I will pause for a few seconds to look for something positive about how I'm currently feeling."

When you have a plan, you can overcome any obstacle that comes your way and know how you'll respond to each situation.

Step #6: Practice Mindfulness Throughout the Day

One of the key strategies for habit development is taking small steps when building new behaviors, and we've designed *The 90-Day Mindfulness Journal* to be as easy as possible. Each day, you'll respond to three simple prompts, which take no more than ten minutes to complete.

That said, to gain the full benefit of mindfulness, you should consider practicing throughout the day—especially when you're anxious or stressed. That's why we invite you to practice mindfulness whenever you:

- Feel anger at an insignificant event.
- Get annoyed during a daily commute.
- Get into an argument with an important person in your life.
- Are enjoying a small moment with a friend or family member.
- Are using a piece of technology that is frustrating you.

There are countless ways to experience mindfulness in your life. The trick is to pause for a few minutes, close your eyes, and complete the quick meditation practice that we outline in the next section. This can become an instant "pick-me-up" whenever you feel stressed or anxious.

Step #7: Reward Yourself for Consistency

Practicing mindfulness should be a rewarding experience. Not only will you live more in the present moment, but also you can also create a reward system based on the number of days you've successfully practiced this behavior.

For example, you could reward yourself whenever you hit important milestones. You could:

- Go see a movie after practicing mindfulness for one week.
- Enjoy a date night out with your significant other after a month.
- Go on a weekend getaway after six months of mindfulness.
- Splurge on an expensive treat after a year.

You get the picture.

Really, the rewards themselves don't matter. What's important is creating positive reinforcement for practicing mindfulness every single day. If you get stuck, we recommend reading Steve's article that covers 155 ways to reward yourself: https://www.developgoodhabits.com/reward-yourself/.

Now that you understand why mindfulness is important, and how to turn it into a daily habit, let's go over the three prompts that are included in this journal so you can get started *writing* in it.

How to Use
This Journal

In this *90-Day Mindfulness Journal*, you'll work on three daily prompts, which shouldn't take more than ten minutes of your time. Two of the prompts will be the same every day, and the third prompt relates to a unique mindfulness meditation topic you'll focus on for the day.

Let's go over each of the three prompts and why they are important:

Prompt #1: Today I have spent my time thinking about

_____

and these thoughts have made me feel _____

_____

The purpose of this prompt is to help you be more mindful and aware of the quality of your thoughts and how they impact your emotions. You'll also learn how to detach from your thoughts and practice non-judgment.

Through this awareness, you'll begin to see patterns of negative or unproductive thinking that have become habitual. In fact, you will likely notice that you have far more negative thoughts throughout the day than positive ones.

For example, you might think:

- "I am so nervous about my presentation this morning. I hope I don't flub it."
- "If I'm not more disciplined, I'll never make enough money to buy a house."
- "I hate the way I look. I'm so fat. Why can't I lose weight?"
- "Nothing ever works out for me. My life sucks."

Pay particular attention to the ruminating thoughts that seem to dominate your mind each day, and choose the one that seems the most powerful or prevalent to write down in this journal.

Then notice the emotions that these thoughts evoke within you.

You might feel...

- Angry
- Sad
- Guilty
- Nervous
- Unloved

- Shamed
- Frustrated
- Unhappy
- Disappointed
- Overwhelmed
- Anxious
- Irritable
- Insecure
- Lonely

Notice how your thoughts trigger these negative emotions, and how the emotions impact your ability to be present, productive, and content during the day.

Sometimes you might notice a negative emotion first before you identify the thought or thoughts that have triggered it. You might feel anxious, for example, but not sure where the anxiety is coming from. Take a moment to ponder the source of the anxiety and whether or not it's attached to any thought or belief.

You don't need to do anything to change your thoughts. But, as part of this activity, notice the thought as though you are an outside observer peering into your brain.

Say to yourself, "There's that thought again," without labeling the thought as good or bad. Just see the thought for what it is—only a thought.

Create awareness around the fact that a thought is simply a mental process. It can't hurt you, and it doesn't reflect complete reality. Detach from the thought and notice how useless and unnecessary it is to the present moment.

Notice the emotions that arise from the thought. Rather than resisting the emotions, just observe them. Rather than thinking, "I am anxious" or "I an angry," say to yourself, "This emotion is anxiety" or "This emotion is anger."

Try to separate yourself from the emotion so that you are not defined by it or the thought that produced it. Just notice and observe. You will discover that detached observation takes away some of the power of negative thoughts and feelings.

Once you write down your thoughts and related emotions, and you observe them, take a deep and cleansing breath and mentally put the thoughts and feelings into an imaginary balloon. Release the balloon and let it float away and out of sight.

Prompt #2: Today I choose to be mindful when I _____

_____ ,

and this is what I noticed during this time of attentiveness and present moment awareness: _____

_____

_____

As we mentioned earlier, opportunities for mindfulness are all around us—in every activity of our day. You can be mindful as you make a cup of tea and mindful as you shower in the morning.

You can bring more focus and attention to a project or task at work. You can pay more attention to your body and its movements as you exercise.

Of course, it's impossible to be mindful with *everything* you do. You can't be in the present moment 24/7, but you can increase the number of times throughout your day when you are more attentive to the world around you. Just a little extra mindfulness during your day goes a long way toward fostering more contentment and inner peace.

For now, start with one activity during your day that you choose to focus on as a mindfulness activity. It can be anything, but we suggest choosing something that isn't too mentally taxing, or that takes more than five to ten minutes, especially if you are new to practicing mindfulness.

Start with a something that is easy enough that you can build your "mindfulness muscle" without overwhelming yourself. Then you can build up to longer periods of mindfulness. We've included some suggestions below.

With each daily activity, mentally stay focused and present with what you are doing and each action or step involved. Use all your senses to experience every aspect of the activity.

For example, if you make a cup of tea, notice:

- The sound of the water as you fill the kettle.
- The feel and look of the cup you choose.
- The smell of the loose tea or tea bag.
- The steam rising as you pour the water over the bag.
- The way the steam feels on your face as you bring the cup to your lips.
- The warmth of the cup in your hands.
- The taste of the first sip of tea.

Do your best to stay present with the activity. But if you get distracted or your mind wanders, just gently redirect your attention back to what you are doing.

Here are some activities to consider for your daily mindfulness activity:

- A full body scan as you awaken in the morning, focusing on every part of your body from head to toe.
- Your morning routine—brushing your teeth, washing your face, etc.
- Your shower or bath.
- Preparing and drinking your coffee or tea.
- Stretching your body.
- Preparing your breakfast.
- Washing dishes or putting them away.
- Folding laundry.
- Making your bed.
- Driving to work.
- Talking with a loved one, friend, co-worker, or stranger.
- Looking at trees.
- Walking outside and noticing sounds and smells.
- Watching the sunset.
- Giving yourself a massage.
- Giving a massage to someone else.
- Watching a flickering candle.
- Listening to music.
- Eating a meal or food item.
- Breathing.

- Writing.
- Staring out the window.

These are just a few ideas to help you spark your own. You can choose just about anything for your mindfulness activity, and it's perfectly fine to repeat an activity on more than one day. The goal is to simply practice presence.

Once you complete your activity, as soon as possible after you perform it, write a few sentences about your experience and what you noticed. Writing about your mindfulness exercise will reinforce the practice, and it gives you another opportunity to be mindful!

Prompt #3: Unique, daily mindfulness meditation prompt.

Meditation is the best way to build your mental muscle so that you have more control over your thoughts. During meditation, you observe the patterns of your mind and learn to tame the incessant chattering of your thoughts.

The more you meditate, the better you become at quieting your mind. As you subdue your disruptive thoughts, you are more able to just rest in the moment and enjoy a blissful experience of peace and relaxation that carries over into daily life.

You will not only enjoy the freedom from intrusive thoughts during your meditation time, but a meditation practice also allows you to be more present during your normal activities. Through meditation, you are honing a skill that you can apply to all aspects of your life, even when you aren't meditating.

That's why we believe it's so important to include meditation as part of this mindfulness journal. Meditation is a "practice," and to reap the benefits, you need to practice it daily. Even a short meditation of five minutes a day helps you develop this valuable habit and allows you to improve as a meditator.

How
to Meditate

The process of meditating is easy. Here's a simple six-step process to help you get started:

#1. Sit on a cushion on the floor or in a straight-back chair.

#2. Rest your hands loosely in your lap.

#3. Close your eyes, and take a deep, cleansing breath.

#4. Begin noticing your breaths. Follow each inhalation and exhalation.

#5. When intrusive thoughts enter your mind, just notice them without judgment, and gently redirect your mind back to your breathing.

#6. After focusing on your breathing, use the daily meditation prompt to expand your experience.

Although these steps aren't complicated, mastering the skill of meditation is more difficult than it might appear.

When you first begin a meditation practice, you will spend most of the time wrestling with your "monkey mind." Intrusive thoughts will pop up constantly, and you will find yourself directing your mind back to your breathing over and over again. This can be frustrating, and you may feel like you aren't accomplishing anything with meditation.

You may also feel physical discomfort, mild restlessness, boredom, and even sleepiness during your meditation time. You may finish your meditation only to discover you've been daydreaming the entire time. All of these are normal obstacles in developing your practice.

But be patient. Just as it takes time to strengthen muscles in your arms when you're lifting weights, it also takes time to get your mental muscle in shape. There are stages to reaching a mature meditation experience.

The more you practice, the more you'll notice that your focus and concentration improve, your intrusive thoughts diminish, and you begin to experience deeper and deeper levels of a meditative state.

During meditation, seasoned meditators say they experience some or all of the following:

- A feeling of tranquility and bliss
- Deep physical relaxation
- Shallow breathing
- A detachment from thoughts and emotions

- A sense of no time or time lapses
- A sense of mental spaciousness
- A loss of self-awareness
- A deep level of introspective awareness

How to Journal
About Your Meditation Efforts

One of the most valuable benefits of journaling about your daily meditation practice is seeing how your experiences in meditation evolve over time. You will see how much less your thoughts intrude and how much better you are able to stay present.

You may also notice other positive side effects, such as re-duced stress and anxiety, better concentration, and more emotional stability.

Here's how to use this journal for your meditation practice:

#1. Read the meditation prompt and spend a moment thinking about how you will apply it during your meditation time.

#2. Find a quiet space where you won't be interrupted or distracted for your meditation.

#3. Set a timer for five to seven minutes.

#4. Begin your meditation as described in the "How to Meditate" section above.

#5. End your meditation with a final, deep, cleansing breath.

As soon as possible, write in your journal about your meditation experience. Write about:

- How you felt physically and emotionally.
- Any intrusive thoughts that you had to manage.
- How easy or difficult it was to redirect your mind to your meditation.
- How "deep" you felt you went with your meditation and what you experienced.
- How you felt about the prompt exercise to include in your meditation.

We have given you additional space to write about your meditation time. Feel free to write as much or as little as you'd like.

That's a brief overview of the three prompts you'll find within this journal. Let's begin your mindfulness journey by starting with Day 1.

Altogether, the idea of meditation is not to create states of ecstasy or absorption, but to experience being.

Chögyam Trungpa

Prompt #1: Today I have spent my time thinking about ____

and these thoughts have made me feel _____

Prompt #2: Today I choose to be mindful when I _____

_____ ,

and this is what I noticed during this time of attentiveness and present moment awareness: _____

Prompt #3: Today I practice a basic mindfulness meditation, focusing only on my breathing, and redirecting my wandering mind back to each breath. Here's what I noticed:

Believe me, all of you, the best way to help the places we live in is to be glad we live there.

Edith Wharton

Prompt #1: Today I have spent my time thinking about _____

_____

and these thoughts have made me feel _____

_____

_____

_____

Prompt #2: Today I choose to be mindful when I _____

_____ ,

and this is what I noticed during this time of attentiveness and present moment awareness: _____

_____

_____

_____

Prompt #3: Today during meditation, I am the watcher of my thoughts. I observe my mind and notice as thoughts float past like clouds. Here's what I noticed: _____

_____

_____

_____

_____

_____

_____

_____

As soon as we wish to be happier, we are no longer happy.

Walter Landor

Prompt #1: Today I have spent my time thinking about _____

_____

and these thoughts have made me feel _____

_____

_____

_____

Prompt #2: Today I choose to be mindful when I _____

_____ ,

and this is what I noticed during this time of attentiveness

and present moment awareness: _____

_____

_____

_____

Prompt #3: Today during meditation, I notice the physical

sensations in my body. I name the sensations as I notice them,

without reacting to them. Here's what I noticed: _____

_____

_____

_____

_____

_____

_____

Envy and jealousy stem from the fundamental inability to rejoice at someone else's happiness or success.

Matthieu Ricard

Prompt #1: Today I have spent my time thinking about _____

and these thoughts have made me feel _____

Prompt #2: Today I choose to be mindful when I _____

_____ ,

and this is what I noticed during this time of attentiveness and present moment awareness: _____

Prompt #3: Today during meditation, I pay attention to any mental resistance I have about meditating. Here's what I noticed: _____

Do not ruin today with mourning tomorrow.
                                    Catherynne M. Valente

Prompt #1: Today I have spent my time thinking about _____

_____

and these thoughts have made me feel _____

_____

_____

_____

Prompt #2: Today I choose to be mindful when I _____

_____ ,

and this is what I noticed during this time of attentiveness
and present moment awareness: _____

_____

_____

_____

Prompt #3: Today during meditation, I put each of my
thoughts into a mental balloon. Whenever a thought arises,
I put it into a balloon, release it, and watch it float away.
Here's what I noticed: _____

_____

_____

_____

_____

_____

_____

Each place is the right place--the place where I now am can be a sacred space.

                                                    Ravi Ravindra

Prompt #1: Today I have spent my time thinking about _____

and these thoughts have made me feel _____

_____

_____

_____

Prompt #2: Today I choose to be mindful when I _____

_____ ,

and this is what I noticed during this time of attentiveness

and present moment awareness: _____

_____

_____

_____

Prompt #3: Today during meditation, I breathe in the white light of peace, and I breathe out any tension or stress. Here's what I noticed: _____

_____

_____

_____

_____

_____

_____

Everything that has a beginning has an ending. Make your peace with that and all will be well.

Jack Kornfield

Prompt #1: Today I have spent my time thinking about ____

and these thoughts have made me feel _____

Prompt #2: Today I choose to be mindful when I _____

_____ ,

and this is what I noticed during this time of attentiveness and present moment awareness: _____

Prompt #3: Today during meditation, I focus on the white light of universal love emanating from my heart and spreading throughout the world. Here's what I noticed: _____

I believe in not trying to control things that are out of my control or none of my business.

Tobe Hanson

Prompt #1: Today I have spent my time thinking about ____

and these thoughts have made me feel _____

_____

_____

_____

Prompt #2: Today I choose to be mindful when I _____

_____ ,

and this is what I noticed during this time of attentiveness

and present moment awareness: _____

_____

_____

_____

Prompt #3: Today during meditation, I contemplate the

vastness of the universe and allow myself to float silently in

the quiet darkness of space. Here's what I noticed: _____

_____

_____

_____

_____

_____

_____

_____

If you want others to be happy, practice compassion. If you want to be happy, practice compassion.

Dalai Lama

Prompt #1: Today I have spent my time thinking about ____

_____

and these thoughts have made me feel _____

_____

_____

_____

Prompt #2: Today I choose to be mindful when I _____

_____ ,

and this is what I noticed during this time of attentiveness and present moment awareness: _____

_____

_____

_____

Prompt #3: Today during meditation, I focus on a beloved family member and mentally repeat, "May you live with ease; may you be happy; may you be free from pain." Here's what I noticed: _____

_____

_____

_____

_____

_____

If you want to conquer the anxiety of life, live in the moment, live in the breath.

Amit Ray

Prompt #1: Today I have spent my time thinking about _____

and these thoughts have made me feel _____

_____

_____

_____

Prompt #2: Today I choose to be mindful when I _____

_____ ,

and this is what I noticed during this time of attentiveness and present moment awareness: _____

_____

_____

_____

Prompt #3: Today during meditation, I listen intently, as though I am awaiting the voice of the universe with a message just for me. Here's what I noticed: _____

_____

_____

_____

_____

_____

_____

_____

If we learn to open our hearts, anyone, including the people who drive us crazy, can be our teacher.

Pema Chodron

Prompt #1: Today I have spent my time thinking about ____

and these thoughts have made me feel _____

Prompt #2: Today I choose to be mindful when I _____

_____,

and this is what I noticed during this time of attentiveness and present moment awareness: _____

Prompt #3: Today during meditation, I notice any emotional pain I am carrying. I breathe into the pain with a healing force of love and release. Here's what I noticed: _____

I wish that life should not be cheap, but sacred. I wish the days to be as centuries, loaded, fragrant.

Ralph Waldo Emerson

Prompt #1: Today I have spent my time thinking about _____

_____

and these thoughts have made me feel _____

_____

_____

_____

Prompt #2: Today I choose to be mindful when I _____

_____ /

and this is what I noticed during this time of attentiveness

and present moment awareness: _____

_____

_____

_____

Prompt #3: Today during meditation, I focus on the light of

pure consciousness, allowing my mind to dissolve and expand

to become one with everything. Here's what I noticed: _____

_____

_____

_____

_____

_____

_____

Feelings come and go like clouds in a windy sky. Conscious breathing is my anchor.

Thich Nhat Hanh

Prompt #1: Today I have spent my time thinking about ____

_____

and these thoughts have made me feel _____

_____

_____

_____

Prompt #2: Today I choose to be mindful when I _____

_____,

and this is what I noticed during this time of attentiveness and present moment awareness: _____

_____

_____

_____

Prompt #3: Today during meditation, I see the small, wounded child of myself, and I embrace this child with love and acceptance. Here's what I noticed: _____

_____

_____

_____

_____

_____

_____

Everything is created twice, first in the mind and then in reality.

Robin S. Sharma

Prompt #1: Today I have spent my time thinking about _____

and these thoughts have made me feel _____

_____

_____

_____

Prompt #2: Today I choose to be mindful when I _____

_____ ,

and this is what I noticed during this time of attentiveness
and present moment awareness: _____

_____

_____

_____

Prompt #3: Today during meditation, I examine a limiting
belief I have about myself. With each exhalation, I release
this belief. With each inhalation, I invite a new mindset about
myself. Here's what I noticed: _____

_____

_____

_____

_____

_____

_____

Look at other people and ask yourself if you are really seeing them or just your thoughts about them.

                                                    Jon Kabat-Zinn

Prompt #1: Today I have spent my time thinking about ____

and these thoughts have made me feel _____

_____

_____

_____

Prompt #2: Today I choose to be mindful when I _____

_____ ,

and this is what I noticed during this time of attentiveness

and present moment awareness: _____

_____

_____

_____

Prompt #3: Today during meditation, I pay attention to

any mental resistance I have about meditating. Here's what

I noticed: _____

_____

_____

_____

_____

_____

_____

Let go of your mind and then be mindful. Close your ears and listen!

Jalaluddin Rumi

Prompt #1: Today I have spent my time thinking about _____

_____

and these thoughts have made me feel _____

_____

_____

_____

Prompt #2: Today I choose to be mindful when I _____

_____ ,

and this is what I noticed during this time of attentiveness and present moment awareness: _____

_____

_____

_____

Prompt #3: Today during meditation, I visualize my body and mind as pure, radiating energy. My body and mind meld with the energy of the universe until we are one. Here's what I noticed: _____

_____

_____

_____

_____

_____

_____

In today's rush, we all think too much — seek too much — want too much — and forget about the joy of just being.

                                                        Eckhart Tolle

Prompt #1: Today I have spent my time thinking about _____

_____

and these thoughts have made me feel _____

_____

_____

_____

Prompt #2: Today I choose to be mindful when I _____

_____—,

and this is what I noticed during this time of attentiveness

and present moment awareness: _____

_____

_____

_____

Prompt #3: Today I meditate on a positive memory that brings me joy, reliving every detail in my mind. Here's what I noticed: _____

_____

_____

_____

_____

_____

_____

Observe the space between your thoughts, then observe the observer.

Hamilton Boudreaux

Prompt #1: Today I have spent my time thinking about _____

and these thoughts have made me feel _____

_____

_____

_____

Prompt #2: Today I choose to be mindful when I _____

_____ ,

and this is what I noticed during this time of attentiveness

and present moment awareness: _____

_____

_____

_____

Prompt #3: Today during meditation, I let my attention rest

on feelings of pride and accomplishment about myself, and I

savor those feelings. Here's what I noticed: _____

_____

_____

_____

_____

_____

_____

_____

Date   /   /

The mind in its natural state can be compared to the sky, covered by layers of cloud which hide its true nature.

Kalu Rinpoche

Prompt #1: Today I have spent my time thinking about _____

and these thoughts have made me feel _____

Prompt #2: Today I choose to be mindful when I _____

_____ ,

and this is what I noticed during this time of attentiveness and present moment awareness: _____

Prompt #3: Today as I meditate, I focus on counting to 10. I count on each exhalation and start over again when I reach the number 10. Here's what I noticed: _____

The path to healthy body, and happy soul is based upon self-study, mindfulness, love and awareness.

Unknown

Prompt #1: Today I have spent my time thinking about _____

and these thoughts have made me feel _____

_____

_____

_____

Prompt #2: Today I choose to be mindful when I _____

_____,

and this is what I noticed during this time of attentiveness and present moment awareness: _____

_____

_____

_____

Prompt #3: Today during meditation, I visualize an eagle peacefully soaring over a vast canyon, dipping and moving with the wind. Here's what I noticed: _____

_____

_____

_____

_____

_____

_____

The little things? The little moments? They aren't little.

Jon Kabat-Zinn

Prompt #1: Today I have spent my time thinking about _____

and these thoughts have made me feel _____

_____

_____

_____

Prompt #2: Today I choose to be mindful when I _____

_____ ,

and this is what I noticed during this time of attentiveness

and present moment awareness: _____

_____

_____

_____

Prompt #3: Today during meditation, I focus on my chest
and abdomen as I breathe. I notice them moving up and
down with each breath, and I follow these movements intently. Here's what I noticed: _____

_____

_____

_____

_____

_____

Suffering usually relates to wanting things to be different than they are.

                                                        Allan Lokos

Prompt #1: Today I have spent my time thinking about _____

_____

and these thoughts have made me feel _____

_____

_____

_____

Prompt #2: Today I choose to be mindful when I _____

_____ ,

and this is what I noticed during this time of attentiveness and present moment awareness: _____

_____

_____

_____

Prompt #3: Today during meditation, my heart is an open receptacle, and I meditate on the healing energy of love pouring into my heart from the universe and filling me with white light. Here's what I noticed: _____

_____

_____

_____

_____

_____

_____

65

Understanding our relationship to eating cultivates a lot of insights and help us start living our highest potential.

Natasa Pantovic

Prompt #1: Today I have spent my time thinking about ＿＿＿

and these thoughts have made me feel ＿＿＿＿＿＿＿＿＿

＿＿＿＿＿＿＿＿＿＿＿＿＿＿＿＿＿＿＿＿＿＿＿＿＿

＿＿＿＿＿＿＿＿＿＿＿＿＿＿＿＿＿＿＿＿＿＿＿＿＿

＿＿＿＿＿＿＿＿＿＿＿＿＿＿＿＿＿＿＿＿＿＿＿＿＿

Prompt #2: Today I choose to be mindful when I ＿＿＿

＿＿＿＿＿＿＿＿＿＿＿＿＿＿＿＿＿＿＿＿＿＿＿＿＿,

and this is what I noticed during this time of attentiveness
and present moment awareness: ＿＿＿＿＿＿＿＿＿＿＿

＿＿＿＿＿＿＿＿＿＿＿＿＿＿＿＿＿＿＿＿＿＿＿＿＿

＿＿＿＿＿＿＿＿＿＿＿＿＿＿＿＿＿＿＿＿＿＿＿＿＿

＿＿＿＿＿＿＿＿＿＿＿＿＿＿＿＿＿＿＿＿＿＿＿＿＿

Prompt #3: As I meditate, I visualize floating in the void of
space, in complete darkness, without sound or sensation, and
see myself as pure and peaceful consciousness. Here's what
I noticed: ＿＿＿＿＿＿＿＿＿＿＿＿＿＿＿＿＿＿＿＿

＿＿＿＿＿＿＿＿＿＿＿＿＿＿＿＿＿＿＿＿＿＿＿＿＿

＿＿＿＿＿＿＿＿＿＿＿＿＿＿＿＿＿＿＿＿＿＿＿＿＿

＿＿＿＿＿＿＿＿＿＿＿＿＿＿＿＿＿＿＿＿＿＿＿＿＿

＿＿＿＿＿＿＿＿＿＿＿＿＿＿＿＿＿＿＿＿＿＿＿＿＿

＿＿＿＿＿＿＿＿＿＿＿＿＿＿＿＿＿＿＿＿＿＿＿＿＿

When you bow, you should just bow; when you sit, you should just sit; when you eat, you should just eat.

Shunryu Suzuki

Prompt #1: Today I have spent my time thinking about ____

_____

and these thoughts have made me feel _____

_____

_____

_____

Prompt #2: Today I choose to be mindful when I _____

_____,

and this is what I noticed during this time of attentiveness and present moment awareness: _____

_____

_____

_____

Prompt #3: Today during meditation, I allow the feeling of bliss to pour from my heart and fill my entire body with an exquisite sense of euphoria. Here's what I noticed: _____

_____

_____

_____

_____

_____

_____

_____

Why, if we are as pragmatic as we claim, don't we begin to ask ourselves seriously: Where does our real future lie?
                                                    Sogyal Rinpoche

Prompt #1: Today I have spent my time thinking about ____

and these thoughts have made me feel _____

Prompt #2: Today I choose to be mindful when I _____

_____ ,

and this is what I noticed during this time of attentiveness

and present moment awareness: _____

Prompt #3: As I meditate, I have a slight smile on my lips. I allow the smile to grow and feel it throughout my mind and body as it extends to the world around me. Here's what I noticed: _____

You can't stop the waves, but you can learn to surf.

Jon Kabat-Zinn

Prompt #1: Today I have spent my time thinking about _____

_____

and these thoughts have made me feel _____

_____

_____

_____

Prompt #2: Today I choose to be mindful when I _____

_____ ,

and this is what I noticed during this time of attentiveness

and present moment awareness: _____

_____

_____

_____

Prompt #3: Today during meditation, I focus on the beating

of my heart and the life force within me, reminding me that I

am alive and well in this moment. Here's what I noticed: ___

_____

_____

_____

_____

_____

_____

_____

When you realize nothing is lacking, the whole world belongs to you.

Lao Tzu

Prompt #1: Today I have spent my time thinking about ____

and these thoughts have made me feel _____

_____

_____

Prompt #2: Today I choose to be mindful when I _____

_____ ,

and this is what I noticed during this time of attentiveness and present moment awareness: _____

_____

_____

Prompt #3: Today during meditation, I rest in a deep sense of appreciation and gratitude for all of the people in my life who guided and supported me. Here's what I noticed: ____

_____

_____

_____

_____

_____

_____

Wherever you are, be there totally.

Eckhart Tolle

Prompt #1: Today I have spent my time thinking about ____

and these thoughts have made me feel _____

_____

_____

_____

Prompt #2: Today I choose to be mindful when I _____

_____,

and this is what I noticed during this time of attentiveness

and present moment awareness: _____

_____

_____

_____

Prompt #3: Today during meditation, I rest in gratitude for

the work that I do and how it sustains me and helps provide

for me. Here's what I noticed: _____

_____

_____

_____

_____

_____

_____

_____

Impermanence is a principle of harmony. When we don't struggle against it, we are in harmony with reality.

Pema Chodron

Prompt #1: Today I have spent my time thinking about _____

_____

and these thoughts have made me feel _____

_____

_____

_____

Prompt #2: Today I choose to be mindful when I _____

_____ ,

and this is what I noticed during this time of attentiveness and present moment awareness: _____

_____

_____

_____

Prompt #3: Today during meditation, I focus on the word "peace" and repeat it mentally on every exhalation. With every repetition, I feel more relaxed and calm. Here's what I noticed: _____

_____

_____

_____

_____

_____

Date / /

Every moment nature is serving fresh dishes with the items of happiness. It is our choice to recognize and taste it.

Amit Ray

Prompt #1: Today I have spent my time thinking about _____

_____

and these thoughts have made me feel _____

_____

_____

_____

Prompt #2: Today I choose to be mindful when I _____

_____,

and this is what I noticed during this time of attentiveness

and present moment awareness: _____

_____

_____

_____

Prompt #3: Today during meditation, I direct my attention to what is happening right now. I notice the sounds, sensations, and smells that arise as I meditate. Here's what I noticed: _____

_____

_____

_____

_____

_____

Do every act of your life as though it were the last act of your life.

Marcus Aurelius

Prompt #1: Today I have spent my time thinking about ____

_____

and these thoughts have made me feel _____

_____

_____

_____

Prompt #2: Today I choose to be mindful when I _____

_____,

and this is what I noticed during this time of attentiveness and present moment awareness: _____

_____

_____

_____

Prompt #3: Today during meditation, I notice any feelings of grief or sadness within me. I breathe into those feelings and allow them to dissipate in a healing, white light. Here's what I noticed: _____

_____

_____

_____

_____

_____

_____

Each morning we are born again. What we do today is what matters most.

Buddha

Prompt #1: Today I have spent my time thinking about ＿＿＿

＿＿＿＿＿＿＿＿＿＿＿＿＿＿＿＿＿＿＿＿＿＿＿＿＿＿＿

and these thoughts have made me feel ＿＿＿＿＿＿＿＿＿

＿＿＿＿＿＿＿＿＿＿＿＿＿＿＿＿＿＿＿＿＿＿＿＿＿＿＿

＿＿＿＿＿＿＿＿＿＿＿＿＿＿＿＿＿＿＿＿＿＿＿＿＿＿＿

＿＿＿＿＿＿＿＿＿＿＿＿＿＿＿＿＿＿＿＿＿＿＿＿＿＿＿

Prompt #2: Today I choose to be mindful when I ＿＿＿＿＿

＿＿＿＿＿＿＿＿＿＿＿＿＿＿＿＿＿＿＿＿＿＿＿＿＿＿,

and this is what I noticed during this time of attentiveness

and present moment awareness: ＿＿＿＿＿＿＿＿＿＿＿＿＿

＿＿＿＿＿＿＿＿＿＿＿＿＿＿＿＿＿＿＿＿＿＿＿＿＿＿＿

＿＿＿＿＿＿＿＿＿＿＿＿＿＿＿＿＿＿＿＿＿＿＿＿＿＿＿

＿＿＿＿＿＿＿＿＿＿＿＿＿＿＿＿＿＿＿＿＿＿＿＿＿＿＿

Prompt #3: Today during meditation, I focus my attention
on my hands resting in my lap. I notice the vibrating, buzzing
life energy in my hands and fingers. Here's what I noticed:

＿＿＿＿＿＿＿＿＿＿＿＿＿＿＿＿＿＿＿＿＿＿＿＿＿＿＿

＿＿＿＿＿＿＿＿＿＿＿＿＿＿＿＿＿＿＿＿＿＿＿＿＿＿＿

＿＿＿＿＿＿＿＿＿＿＿＿＿＿＿＿＿＿＿＿＿＿＿＿＿＿＿

＿＿＿＿＿＿＿＿＿＿＿＿＿＿＿＿＿＿＿＿＿＿＿＿＿＿＿

＿＿＿＿＿＿＿＿＿＿＿＿＿＿＿＿＿＿＿＿＿＿＿＿＿＿＿

＿＿＿＿＿＿＿＿＿＿＿＿＿＿＿＿＿＿＿＿＿＿＿＿＿＿＿

＿＿＿＿＿＿＿＿＿＿＿＿＿＿＿＿＿＿＿＿＿＿＿＿＿＿＿

Flow with whatever may happen and let your mind be free: Stay centered by accepting whatever you are doing. This is the ultimate.   Chuang

Prompt #1: Today I have spent my time thinking about ____

and these thoughts have made me feel _____

_____

_____

_____

Prompt #2: Today I choose to be mindful when I _____

_____,

and this is what I noticed during this time of attentiveness and present moment awareness: _____

_____

_____

_____

Prompt #3: Today during meditation, I allow each inhalation of breath to be an energizing force that fills my body with aliveness and joy. Here's what I noticed: _____

_____

_____

_____

_____

_____

_____

If the doors of perception were cleansed, everything would appear to man as it is, infinite.

William Blake

Prompt #1: Today I have spent my time thinking about ____

and these thoughts have made me feel _____

_____

_____

_____

Prompt #2: Today I choose to be mindful when I _____

_____,

and this is what I noticed during this time of attentiveness and present moment awareness: _____

_____

_____

_____

Prompt #3: Today during meditation, I rest in the feeling of forgiveness for myself and others and allow its soothing balm to fill me with peace. Here's what I noticed: _____

_____

_____

_____

_____

_____

_____

_____

Every time we become aware of a thought, as opposed to being lost in a thought, we experience that opening of the mind.
                                              Joseph Goldstein

Prompt #1: Today I have spent my time thinking about ____

and these thoughts have made me feel _____

_____

_____

_____

Prompt #2: Today I choose to be mindful when I _____

_____ ,

and this is what I noticed during this time of attentiveness and present moment awareness: _____

_____

_____

_____

Prompt #3: Today during meditation, I repeat the mantra "Om" silently or softly out loud with each exhalation, and allow the vibration of this mantra to meld with pure consciousness. Here's what I noticed: _____

_____

_____

_____

_____

_____

Life is a dance. Mindfulness is witnessing that dance.

Amit Ray

Prompt #1: Today I have spent my time thinking about ＿＿＿

and these thoughts have made me feel ＿＿＿＿＿＿＿

＿＿＿＿＿＿＿＿＿＿＿＿＿＿＿＿

＿＿＿＿＿＿＿＿＿＿＿＿＿＿＿＿

＿＿＿＿＿＿＿＿＿＿＿＿＿＿＿＿

Prompt #2: Today I choose to be mindful when I ＿＿＿＿

＿＿＿＿＿＿＿＿＿＿＿＿＿＿＿＿,

and this is what I noticed during this time of attentiveness

and present moment awareness: ＿＿＿＿＿＿＿＿

＿＿＿＿＿＿＿＿＿＿＿＿＿＿＿＿

＿＿＿＿＿＿＿＿＿＿＿＿＿＿＿＿

＿＿＿＿＿＿＿＿＿＿＿＿＿＿＿＿

Prompt #3: Today during meditation, I repeat the affirmation, "I am here, now" with every breath and try to stay grounded in the present moment. Here's what I noticed: ＿＿＿

Mindful eating is a way to become reacquainted with the guidance of our internal nutritionist.

Jan Chozen Bays

Prompt #1: Today I have spent my time thinking about ____

_____

and these thoughts have made me feel _____

_____

_____

_____

Prompt #2: Today I choose to be mindful when I _____

_____ ,

and this is what I noticed during this time of attentiveness

and present moment awareness: _____

_____

_____

_____

Prompt #3: Today during meditation, I rest in the feelings of self-love and my essential goodness. With every breath, I love myself more. Here's what I noticed: _____

_____

_____

_____

_____

_____

_____

_____

Respond; don't react. Listen; don't talk. Think; don't assume.

Raji Lukkoor

Prompt #1: Today I have spent my time thinking about ____

_____

and these thoughts have made me feel _____

_____

_____

_____

Prompt #2: Today I choose to be mindful when I _____

_____ ,

and this is what I noticed during this time of attentiveness

and present moment awareness: _____

_____

_____

_____

Prompt #3: Today during meditation, I extend feelings of compassion for all people around the world. I visualize com-passion pouring from my heart and spreading to all beings. Here's what I noticed: _____

_____

_____

_____

_____

_____

_____

Tea is an act complete in its simplicity. When I drink tea, there is only me and the tea. The rest of the world dissolves.
                                                    Thích Nhat Hanh

Prompt #1: Today I have spent my time thinking about _____

_____

and these thoughts have made me feel _____

_____

_____

_____

Prompt #2: Today I choose to be mindful when I _____

_____ ,

and this is what I noticed during this time of attentiveness

and present moment awareness: _____

_____

_____

_____

Prompt #3: Today during meditation, I inhale while counting to four, then hold the breath for four seconds. I breathe
out for four seconds and hold empty for four seconds. I repeat this until my mind calms. Here's what I noticed: _____

_____

_____

_____

_____

_____

Things falling apart is a kind of testing and also a kind of healing.

Pema Chodron

Prompt #1: Today I have spent my time thinking about ____

and these thoughts have made me feel ____

Prompt #2: Today I choose to be mindful when I ____

____,

and this is what I noticed during this time of attentiveness and present moment awareness: ____

Prompt #3: Today as I meditate, I try to empty my mind completely and focus on nothing. As thoughts arise, I gently usher them out. Here's what I noticed: ____

Until you realize how easily it is for your mind to be manipulated, you remain the puppet of someone else's game.

Evita Ochel

Prompt #1: Today I have spent my time thinking about _____

_____

and these thoughts have made me feel _____

_____

_____

_____

Prompt #2: Today I choose to be mindful when I _____

_____ ,

and this is what I noticed during this time of attentiveness

and present moment awareness: _____

_____

_____

_____

Prompt #3: Today during meditation, I breathe relaxation

into every area of my body, beginning with my toes and mov-

ing up to my head. Here's what I noticed: _____

_____

_____

_____

_____

_____

_____

We are awakened to the profound realization that the true path to liberation is to let go of everything.

Jack Kornfield

Prompt #1: Today I have spent my time thinking about _____

_____

and these thoughts have made me feel _____

_____

_____

_____

Prompt #2: Today I choose to be mindful when I _____

_____ ,

and this is what I noticed during this time of attentiveness

and present moment awareness: _____

_____

_____

_____

Prompt #3: Today during meditation, I notice my attachments and longings for people, material things, and conditions. I allow my attention to dwell on my attachments and longings. Here's what I noticed: _____

_____

_____

_____

_____

_____

When I'm hungry, I eat what I love. When I'm bored, I do something I love. When I'm lonely, I connect with someone I love. When I feel sad, I remember that I am loved.   Michelle May

Prompt #1: Today I have spent my time thinking about ____

_____

and these thoughts have made me feel _____

_____

_____

_____

Prompt #2: Today I choose to be mindful when I _____

_____ ,

and this is what I noticed during this time of attentiveness

and present moment awareness: _____

_____

_____

_____

Prompt #3: Today during meditation, I contemplate the principle of impermanence and that nothing lasts forever. I notice how this awareness deepens my experience of the present moment. Here's what I noticed: _____

_____

_____

_____

_____

_____

_____

Date   /   /

You can't stop the waves, but you can learn to surf.

Jon Kabat-Zinn

Prompt #1: Today I have spent my time thinking about _____

_____

and these thoughts have made me feel _____

_____

_____

_____

Prompt #2: Today I choose to be mindful when I _____

_____ ,

and this is what I noticed during this time of attentiveness

and present moment awareness: _____

_____

_____

_____

Prompt #3: Today as I meditate, I allow myself to completely let go of anything that I am mentally clinging to. With
every exhalation, I breathe out anything I am clinging to and
allow it to disappear. Here's what I noticed: _____

_____

_____

_____

_____

_____

_____

Be kind whenever possible. It is always possible.

Dalai Lama

Prompt #1: Today I have spent my time thinking about _____

_____

and these thoughts have made me feel _____

_____
_____
_____

Prompt #2: Today I choose to be mindful when I _____

_____ ,

and this is what I noticed during this time of attentiveness and present moment awareness: _____

_____
_____
_____

Prompt #3: Today during meditation, I focus on my "third eye," the space between my eyebrows. I visualize white light streaming from this space to connect with the universe. Here's what I noticed: _____

_____
_____
_____
_____
_____

In the end, just three things matter: How well we have lived. How well we have loved. How well we have learned to let go.

Jack Kornfield

Prompt #1: Today I have spent my time thinking about ____

_____

and these thoughts have made me feel _____

_____

_____

_____

Prompt #2: Today I choose to be mindful when I _____

_____ ,

and this is what I noticed during this time of attentiveness

and present moment awareness: _____

_____

_____

_____

Prompt #3: Today during meditation, I offer non-resistance

to my "monkey mind." I smile at my thoughts and see them as

the silly monkeys they are. I don't resist them—I just smile and

notice. Here's what I noticed: _____

_____

_____

_____

_____

_____

If you clean the floor with love, you have given the world an invisible painting.

Osho

Prompt #1: Today I have spent my time thinking about ____

and these thoughts have made me feel _____

Prompt #2: Today I choose to be mindful when I _____

_____ /

and this is what I noticed during this time of attentiveness and present moment awareness: _____

Prompt #3: Today as I meditate, I see myself in a small dark room with no light. I am encompassed by the peaceful darkness with no sensations. As I meditate, the dark room expands and my consciousness expands with it. Here's what I noticed: _____

If one were truly aware of the value of human life, to waste it blithely on distractions and the pursuit of vulgar ambitions would be the height of confusion.   Dilgo Khyentse Rinpoche

Prompt #1: Today I have spent my time thinking about ____

_____

and these thoughts have made me feel _____

_____

_____

_____

Prompt #2: Today I choose to be mindful when I _____

_____ ,

and this is what I noticed during this time of attentiveness and present moment awareness: _____

_____

_____

_____

Prompt #3: Today during meditation, I visualize a flickering candle and focus my attention on the flame throughout the meditation. Here's what I noticed: _____

_____

_____

_____

_____

_____

_____

Always hold fast to the present. Every situation, indeed every moment, is of infinite value, for it is the representative of a whole eternity.   Johann Wolfgang von Goethe

Prompt #1: Today I have spent my time thinking about _____

_____

and these thoughts have made me feel _____

_____

_____

_____

Prompt #2: Today I choose to be mindful when I _____

_____ ,

and this is what I noticed during this time of attentiveness and present moment awareness: _____

_____

_____

_____

Prompt #3: Today as I meditate, I concentrate on a bottom-less well, and I am gently falling down the well into eternity. I experience a sense of peace and letting go. Here's what I noticed: _____

_____

_____

_____

_____

_____

Begin at once to live, and count each separate day as a separate life.

Seneca

Prompt #1: Today I have spent my time thinking about ____

_____

and these thoughts have made me feel _____

_____
_____
_____

Prompt #2: Today I choose to be mindful when I _____

_____ ,

and this is what I noticed during this time of attentiveness
and present moment awareness: _____

_____
_____
_____

Prompt #3: Today during meditation, I go within to find the
core of my happiness. I see that happiness shining forth from
my body and filling the room with bright light. Here's what
I noticed: _____

_____
_____
_____
_____
_____
_____

If you concentrate on finding whatever is good in every situation, you will discover that your life will suddenly be filled with gratitude, a feeling that nurtures the soul.   Rabbi Harold

Prompt #1: Today I have spent my time thinking about ____

_____

and these thoughts have made me feel _____

_____

_____

_____

Prompt #2: Today I choose to be mindful when I _____

_____,

and this is what I noticed during this time of attentiveness

and present moment awareness: _____

_____

_____

_____

Prompt #3: Today I meditate on those in the world who are

suffering and in pain. I breathe in compassion and breathe

out healing love. Here's what I noticed: _____

_____

_____

_____

_____

_____

_____

_____

In this moment, there is plenty of time. In this moment, you are precisely as you should be. In this moment, there is infinite possibility.
Victoria Moran

Prompt #1: Today I have spent my time thinking about ____

and these thoughts have made me feel _____

_____

_____

_____

Prompt #2: Today I choose to be mindful when I _____

_____ ,

and this is what I noticed during this time of attentiveness
and present moment awareness: _____

_____

_____

_____

Prompt #3: Today during meditation, I notice any pains and discomforts in my body. I do not resist them but rather breathe into them with tenderness and care. Here's what I noticed: _____

_____

_____

_____

_____

_____

Life is better when we don't try to do everything. Learn to enjoy the slice of life you experience, and life turns out to be wonderful.
Leo Babauta

Prompt #1: Today I have spent my time thinking about _____

_____

and these thoughts have made me feel _____

_____

_____

_____

Prompt #2: Today I choose to be mindful when I _____

_____ ,

and this is what I noticed during this time of attentiveness

and present moment awareness: _____

_____

_____

_____

Prompt #3: Today during meditation, I repeat the mantra,

"I am." With every breath, I say these words to ground myself

in the here and now. Here's what I noticed: _____

_____

_____

_____

_____

_____

_____

Meditate ... do not delay, lest you later regret it.

Buddha

Prompt #1: Today I have spent my time thinking about _____

and these thoughts have made me feel _____

_____

_____

_____

Prompt #2: Today I choose to be mindful when I _____

_____ ,

and this is what I noticed during this time of attentiveness

and present moment awareness: _____

_____

_____

_____

Prompt #3: Today during meditation, I notice all physical

and mental distractions, and as they arise, I label them (pain,

itch, anxiety, thought, etc.). Here's what I noticed: _____

_____

_____

_____

_____

_____

_____

Meditation practice isn't about trying to throw ourselves away and become something better. It's about befriending who we are already.   Pema Chödrön

Prompt #1: Today I have spent my time thinking about ____

_____

and these thoughts have made me feel _____

_____
_____
_____

Prompt #2: Today I choose to be mindful when I _____

_____,

and this is what I noticed during this time of attentiveness
and present moment awareness: _____

_____
_____
_____

Prompt #3: Today during meditation, I think about a difficult person in my life and repeat to myself, "May you live with ease; may you be happy; may you be free from pain." Here's what I noticed: _____

_____
_____
_____
_____
_____

Mindful eating is about awareness. When you eat mindfully, you slow down, pay attention to the food you're eating, and savor every bite.   Susan Albers

Prompt #1: Today I have spent my time thinking about ____

_____

and these thoughts have made me feel _____

_____

_____

_____

Prompt #2: Today I choose to be mindful when I _____

_____ ,

and this is what I noticed during this time of attentiveness and present moment awareness: _____

_____

_____

_____

Prompt #3: Today during meditation, I contemplate the life force moving throughout the inside of my body and mind. I notice it as a vibrating energy that animates and enlivens me. Here's what I noticed: _____

_____

_____

_____

_____

_____

_____

Life is not lost by dying; life is lost minute by minute, day by dragging day, in all the small uncaring ways.

Stephen Vincent Benet

Prompt #1: Today I have spent my time thinking about _____

and these thoughts have made me feel _____

_____

_____

_____

Prompt #2: Today I choose to be mindful when I _____

_____ ,

and this is what I noticed during this time of attentiveness and present moment awareness: _____

_____

_____

_____

Prompt #3: Today during meditation, I see myself walking a long and beautiful path in nature. I gaze at my feet and notice every step I take along the path. Here's what I noticed:

_____

_____

_____

_____

_____

_____

Date   /   /   .

Mindfulness isn't difficult, we just need to remember to do it.

Sharon Salzberg

Prompt #1: Today I have spent my time thinking about _____

_____

and these thoughts have made me feel _____

_____

_____

_____

Prompt #2: Today I choose to be mindful when I _____

_____,

and this is what I noticed during this time of attentiveness

and present moment awareness: _____

_____

_____

_____

Prompt #3: Today during meditation, I concentrate on the

uncertainty of life and rest in this uncertainty with calm open-

ness and acceptance. Here's what I noticed: _____

_____

_____

_____

_____

_____

_____

The best way to capture moments is to pay attention. This is how we cultivate mindfulness.

Jon Kabat-Zinn

Prompt #1: Today I have spent my time thinking about _____

and these thoughts have made me feel _____

_____

_____

_____

Prompt #2: Today I choose to be mindful when I _____

_____,

and this is what I noticed during this time of attentiveness

and present moment awareness: _____

_____

_____

_____

Prompt #3: Today during meditation, I continue to ask my-self, "Who am I?" until I strip away all ego-based roles and feel the presence of my pure consciousness. Here's what I noticed: _____

_____

_____

_____

_____

_____

Our own worst enemy cannot harm us as much as our unwise thoughts. No one can help us as much as our own compassionate thoughts.   Buddha

Prompt #1: Today I have spent my time thinking about ____

_____

and these thoughts have made me feel _____

_____

_____

_____

Prompt #2: Today I choose to be mindful when I _____

_____ ,

and this is what I noticed during this time of attentiveness

and present moment awareness: _____

_____

_____

_____

Prompt #3: Today during meditation, I slowly repeat the Hindu mantra "om namah shivaya" over and over again. I don't attach meaning to the mantra but just repeat it to focus my concentration. Here's what I noticed: _____

_____

_____

_____

_____

_____

The most precious gift we can offer others is our presence. When mindfulness embraces those we love, they will bloom like flowers.
                                                        Thich Nhat Hanh

Prompt #1: Today I have spent my time thinking about _____

_____

and these thoughts have made me feel _____

_____

_____

_____

Prompt #2: Today I choose to be mindful when I _____

_____ ,

and this is what I noticed during this time of attentiveness and present moment awareness: _____

_____

_____

_____

Prompt #3: Today during meditation, I rest in the small and vast space between thoughts. I linger in that space as long as my mind allows and return to it over and over again. Here's what I noticed: _____

_____

_____

_____

_____

_____

Date   /   /

Mindfulness isn't difficult, we just need to remember to do it.

Sharon Salzberg

Prompt #1: Today I have spent my time thinking about ____

and these thoughts have made me feel _____

_____

_____

_____

Prompt #2: Today I choose to be mindful when I _____

_____ ,

and this is what I noticed during this time of attentiveness

and present moment awareness: _____

_____

_____

_____

Prompt #3: Today as I meditate, I contemplate gratitude for

the people, possessions, and circumstances that are mean-

ingful to me. Breathing in, I am filled with joy. Breathing out,

my gratitude expands to the world. Here's what I noticed:

_____

_____

_____

_____

_____

_____

Mindful and creative, a child who has neither a past, nor examples to follow, nor value judgments, simply lives, speaks and plays in freedom.   Arnaud Desjardins

Prompt #1: Today I have spent my time thinking about ____

_____

and these thoughts have made me feel _____

_____

_____

_____

Prompt #2: Today I choose to be mindful when I _____

_____ ,

and this is what I noticed during this time of attentiveness and present moment awareness: _____

_____

_____

_____

Prompt #3: Today during meditation, I envision a healing beam of light flowing down from the sky, through the top of my head, filling my body with energy and grounding me to the earth. Here's what I noticed: _____

_____

_____

_____

_____

_____

Training your mind to be in the present moment is the #1 key to making healthier choices.

Susan Albers

Prompt #1: Today I have spent my time thinking about ____

and these thoughts have made me feel _____

Prompt #2: Today I choose to be mindful when I _____

_____ ,

and this is what I noticed during this time of attentiveness and present moment awareness: _____

Prompt #3: Today during meditation, I ponder the thread of connection I have with all sentient beings. I see a golden thread that draws us together in universal kinship. Here's what I noticed: _____

Use every distraction as an object of meditation and they cease to be distractions.

Mingyur Rinpoche

Prompt #1: Today I have spent my time thinking about ____

and these thoughts have made me feel _____

Prompt #2: Today I choose to be mindful when I _____

_____ ,

and this is what I noticed during this time of attentiveness and present moment awareness: _____

Prompt #3: Today during meditation, I notice the ways I need to control certain people and aspects of my life. As I breathe out, I release the need to control. Here's what I noticed: _____

We have only now, only this single eternal moment opening and unfolding before us, day and night.

Jack Kornfield

Prompt #1: Today I have spent my time thinking about ＿＿＿

and these thoughts have made me feel ＿＿＿＿＿＿＿

＿＿＿＿＿＿＿＿＿＿＿＿＿＿＿＿＿＿

＿＿＿＿＿＿＿＿＿＿＿＿＿＿＿＿＿＿

＿＿＿＿＿＿＿＿＿＿＿＿＿＿＿＿＿＿

Prompt #2: Today I choose to be mindful when I ＿＿＿＿

＿＿＿＿＿＿＿＿＿＿＿＿＿＿＿＿＿＿ ,

and this is what I noticed during this time of attentiveness and present moment awareness: ＿＿＿＿＿＿＿＿

＿＿＿＿＿＿＿＿＿＿＿＿＿＿＿＿＿＿

＿＿＿＿＿＿＿＿＿＿＿＿＿＿＿＿＿＿

＿＿＿＿＿＿＿＿＿＿＿＿＿＿＿＿＿＿

Prompt #3: Today during meditation, I sit peacefully and notice. I notice thoughts, sensations, emotions, and distractions. I welcome them all. I do not resist them. Here's what I noticed: ＿＿＿＿＿＿＿＿＿＿＿＿＿＿＿

＿＿＿＿＿＿＿＿＿＿＿＿＿＿＿＿＿＿

＿＿＿＿＿＿＿＿＿＿＿＿＿＿＿＿＿＿

＿＿＿＿＿＿＿＿＿＿＿＿＿＿＿＿＿＿

＿＿＿＿＿＿＿＿＿＿＿＿＿＿＿＿＿＿

＿＿＿＿＿＿＿＿＿＿＿＿＿＿＿＿＿＿

Today, like every other day, we wake up empty and frightened.
Don't open the door to the study and begin reading. Take down a
musical instrument.   Rumi

Prompt #1: Today I have spent my time thinking about ____

and these thoughts have made me feel _____

Prompt #2: Today I choose to be mindful when I _____

_____ ,

and this is what I noticed during this time of attentiveness
and present moment awareness: _____

Prompt #3: As I meditate, I see myself striking a gong with
a mallet. The sound of the gong reverberates and fades, and
then I strike the gong again, repeating this action over and
over again. Here's what I noticed: _____

When we get too caught up in the busyness of the world, we lose connection with one another - and ourselves.

Jack Kornfield

Prompt #1: Today I have spent my time thinking about _____

_____

and these thoughts have made me feel _____

_____

_____

_____

Prompt #2: Today I choose to be mindful when I _____

_____ ,

and this is what I noticed during this time of attentiveness

and present moment awareness: _____

_____

_____

_____

Prompt #3: Today during meditation, I am a bird flying through a cloudless sky. I notice all that I see below and around me and the feelings I have as I fly. Here's what I noticed: _____

_____

_____

_____

_____

_____

The mind is just like a muscle - the more you exercise it, the stronger it gets and the more it can expand.

                                          Idowu Koyenikan

Prompt #1: Today I have spent my time thinking about ____

and these thoughts have made me feel _____

_____

_____

_____

Prompt #2: Today I choose to' be mindful when I _____

_____,

and this is what I noticed during this time of attentiveness and present moment awareness: _____

_____

_____

_____

Prompt #3: Today during meditation, I concentrate on my posture, aligning my head, neck, and spine as though a rod were anchoring me to my chair. I then align my breathing with my posture. With each breath, I maintain my posture. Here's what I noticed: _____

_____

_____

_____

_____

Date   /   /

One who is patient glows with an inner radiance.

Allan Lokos

Prompt #1: Today I have spent my time thinking about ____

_____

and these thoughts have made me feel _____

_____

_____

_____

Prompt #2: Today I choose to be mindful when I _____

_____ ,

and this is what I noticed during this time of attentiveness

and present moment awareness: _____

_____

_____

_____

Prompt #3: Today during meditation, I focus on the pre-
ciousness of each moment and how fleeting each moment is.
Here's what I noticed: _____

_____

_____

_____

_____

_____

_____

Date   /   /

Looking at beauty in the world, is the first step of purifying the mind.

Amit Ray

Prompt #1: Today I have spent my time thinking about _____

_____

and these thoughts have made me feel _____

_____

_____

_____

Prompt #2: Today I choose to be mindful when I _____

_____,

and this is what I noticed during this time of attentiveness and present moment awareness: _____

_____

_____

_____

Prompt #3: Today during meditation, I notice areas of my body where I feel anxiety or restlessness. I focus my breathing into those areas of my body. Here's what I noticed: _____

_____

_____

_____

_____

_____

_____

The things that matter most in our lives are not fantastic or grand. They are moments when we touch one another.

                                              Jack Kornfield

Prompt #1: Today I have spent my time thinking about _____

_____

and these thoughts have made me feel _____

_____

_____

_____

Prompt #2: Today I choose to be mindful when I _____

_____ ,

and this is what I noticed during this time of attentiveness

and present moment awareness: _____

_____

_____

_____

Prompt #3: Today during meditation, I recognize the pure

potential in each moment and how it invites me to recognize

and savor it. Here's what I noticed: _____

_____

_____

_____

_____

_____

_____

We might begin by scanning our body . . . and then asking, "What is happening?" We might also ask, "What wants my attention right now?" or, "What is asking for acceptance?   Tara Brach

Prompt #1: Today I have spent my time thinking about ____

and these thoughts have made me feel _____

Prompt #2: Today I choose to be mindful when I _____

_____ ,

and this is what I noticed during this time of attentiveness and present moment awareness: _____

Prompt #3: As I meditate, I recognize my obsessions and bad habits. I see how attached I am to them with my thoughts. I release my thoughts about these obsessions and habits so I can let them go. Here's what I noticed: _____

We have only now, only this single eternal moment opening and unfolding before us, day and night.

Jack Kornfield

Prompt #1: Today I have spent my time thinking about ____

_____

and these thoughts have made me feel _____

_____

_____

_____

Prompt #2: Today I choose to be mindful when I _____

_____—,

and this is what I noticed during this time of attentiveness

and present moment awareness: _____

_____

_____

_____

Prompt #3: Today during meditation, I allow my sense of "self" to evaporate. I am nothing but pure conscious aware-ness. Here's what I noticed: _____

_____

_____

_____

_____

_____

_____

The basic root of happiness lies in our minds; outer circumstances are nothing more than adverse or favorable.

Matthieu Ricard

Prompt #1: Today I have spent my time thinking about _____

_____

and these thoughts have made me feel _____

_____

_____

_____

Prompt #2: Today I choose to be mindful when I _____

_____ ,

and this is what I noticed during this time of attentiveness and present moment awareness: _____

_____

_____

_____

Prompt #3: As I meditate today, I become one with my breathing. I am nothing except a breath. On the inhale, I am. On the exhale, I am. Here's what I noticed: _____

_____

_____

_____

_____

_____

_____

When we get too caught up in the busyness of the world, we lose connection with one another - and ourselves.

Jack Kornfield

Prompt #1: Today I have spent my time thinking about ____

and these thoughts have made me feel _____

_____

_____

_____

Prompt #2: Today I choose to be mindful when I _____

_____ ,

and this is what I noticed during this time of attentiveness

and present moment awareness: _____

_____

_____

_____

Prompt #3: Today during meditation, I follow my breath in through my nose and notice the feeling of air entering my nostrils and moving into my lungs. Here's what I noticed:

_____

_____

_____

_____

_____

_____

_____

We have only now, only this single eternal moment opening and unfolding before us, day and night.

Jack Kornfield

Prompt #1: Today I have spent my time thinking about ____

_____

and these thoughts have made me feel _____

_____

_____

_____

Prompt #2: Today I choose to be mindful when I _____

_____ ,

and this is what I noticed during this time of attentiveness and present moment awareness: _____

_____

_____

_____

Prompt #3: Today during meditation, I visualize my body surrounded by a white, healing light. This is a comforting, calming light that fills me with inner peace. Here's what I noticed: _____

_____

_____

_____

_____

_____

Mindfulness means being awake. It means knowing what you are doing.
Jon Kabat-Zinn

Prompt #1: Today I have spent my time thinking about _____

_____

and these thoughts have made me feel _____

_____

_____

_____

Prompt #2: Today I choose to be mindful when I _____

_____,

and this is what I noticed during this time of attentiveness

and present moment awareness: _____

_____

_____

_____

Prompt #3: As I meditate, I contemplate my ego and the

false beliefs my ego creates. I breathe the truth of selflessness

into my ego with every breath, knowing the only truth is this

current moment. Here's what I noticed: _____

_____

_____

_____

_____

_____

_____

The practice of mindfulness begins in the small, remote cave of your unconscious mind and blossoms with the sunlight of your conscious life, reaching far beyond the people and places you can see. Earon Davis

Prompt #1: Today I have spent my time thinking about ____

and these thoughts have made me feel _____

_____

_____

_____

Prompt #2: Today I choose to be mindful when I _____

_____,

and this is what I noticed during this time of attentiveness and present moment awareness: _____

_____

_____

_____

Prompt #3: Today during meditation, I contemplate on the formlessness and intangibility of my mind, and I invite my mind to be a peaceful guest in my house (the body). Here's what I noticed: _____

_____

_____

_____

_____

_____

_____

Be mindful. Be grateful. Be positive. Be true. Be kind.

Roy T. Bennett

Prompt #1: Today I have spent my time thinking about ____

and these thoughts have made me feel _____

_____

_____

_____

Prompt #2: Today I choose to be mindful when I _____

_____ ,

and this is what I noticed during this time of attentiveness

and present moment awareness: _____

_____

_____

_____

Prompt #3: Today during meditation, I recognize that all of my emotional suffering arises from deluded states of my mind. I notice the thoughts produced by my mind that cause my suffering . Here's what I noticed: _____

_____

_____

_____

_____

_____

_____

As long as we have practiced neither concentration nor mindfulness, the ego takes itself for granted and remains its usual normal size, as big as the people around one will allow.   Ayya Khema

Prompt #1: Today I have spent my time thinking about _____

and these thoughts have made me feel _____

_____

_____

_____

Prompt #2: Today I choose to be mindful when I _____

_____,

and this is what I noticed during this time of attentiveness and present moment awareness: _____

_____

_____

_____

Prompt #3: Today during meditation, I visualize a window in my forehead, and I peer into it to watch my thoughts. Are my thoughts still wild monkeys, or is the space in my mind clear? I don't judge but just look through the window as an outside observer. Here's what I noticed: _____

_____

_____

_____

_____

Date   /   /

Drink your tea slowly and reverently, as if it is the axis on which the world earth revolves - slowly, evenly, without rushing toward the future; live the actual moment. Only this moment is life.   Thich Nhat Hanh

Prompt #1: Today I have spent my time thinking about _____

and these thoughts have made me feel _____

_____

_____

_____

Prompt #2: Today I choose to be mindful when I _____

_____ ,

and this is what I noticed during this time of attentiveness

and present moment awareness: _____

_____

_____

_____

Prompt #3: Today during meditation, I visualize myself floating on a raft in the ocean, feeling the gentle movements of
small waves. It is just me and the sounds, smells, and sensations of floating on water. Here's what I noticed: _____

_____

_____

_____

_____

_____

_____

Don't believe everything you think. Thoughts are just that - thoughts.

Allan Lokos

Prompt #1: Today I have spent my time thinking about ____

_____

and these thoughts have made me feel _____

_____

_____

_____

Prompt #2: Today I choose to be mindful when I _____

_____,

and this is what I noticed during this time of attentiveness

and present moment awareness: _____

_____

_____

_____

Prompt #3: Today during meditation, I envision someone I

love deeply. I think how much I cherish and adore this person

and focus all of my mental energy into love that I send to him

or her. Here's what I noticed: _____

_____

_____

_____

_____

_____

Being mindful means that we suspend judgment for a time, set aside our immediate goals for the future, and take in the present moment as it is rather than as we would like it to be.   Mark Williams

Prompt #1: Today I have spent my time thinking about _____

_____

and these thoughts have made me feel _____

_____

_____

_____

Prompt #2: Today I choose to be mindful when I _____

_____,

and this is what I noticed during this time of attentiveness

and present moment awareness: _____

_____

_____

_____

Prompt #3: Today during meditation, I notice any rushed feelings to be done with the meditation. I notice the anxiety to move on to my tasks. I breathe through these feelings and allow them to pass through me. Here's what I noticed: _____

_____

_____

_____

_____

_____

By breaking down our sense of self-importance, all we lose is a parasite that has long infected our minds. What we gain in return is freedom, openness of mind, spontaneity, simplicity, altruism: all qualities inherent in happiness.
Matthieu Ricard

Prompt #1: Today I have spent my time thinking about ____

_____

and these thoughts have made me feel _____

_____

_____

_____

Prompt #2: Today I choose to be mindful when I _____

_____—,

and this is what I noticed during this time of attentiveness

and present moment awareness: _____

_____

_____

_____

Prompt #3: As I meditate, I release any need for this meditation to be more than it is. It is not good or bad or wrong or right. It just is and I accept it as it is. Here's what I noticed:

_____

_____

_____

_____

_____

_____

Our lives are lived in intense and anxious struggle, in a swirl of speed and aggression, in competing, grasping, possessing and achieving, forever burdening ourselves with extraneous activities and preoccupations.
                                                    Sogyal Rinpoche

Prompt #1: Today I have spent my time thinking about _____

_____

and these thoughts have made me feel _____

_____

_____

_____

Prompt #2: Today I choose to be mindful when I _____

_____ ,

and this is what I noticed during this time of attentiveness

and present moment awareness: _____

_____

_____

_____

Prompt #3: Today during meditation, I see my mind as a series of rooms. I open the doors to all of the rooms and allow my thoughts to escape. My thoughts leave my mind, and the rooms are clear and empty. Here's what I noticed: _____

_____

_____

_____

_____

_____

Instead of thinking of food as the enemy, allow yourself to enjoy the process of planning and preparing meals or going out to lunch with a friend. Stay in the present moment and understand that the purpose of food is nourishment.   Susan Albers

Prompt #1: Today I have spent my time thinking about ____

and these thoughts have made me feel _____

Prompt #2: Today I choose to be mindful when I _____

_____,
and this is what I noticed during this time of attentiveness and present moment awareness: _____

Prompt #3: As I meditate today, I give myself over to trust in the process. I trust that my meditation time is for my betterment. I trust that meditation is what I should be doing right now. Here's what I noticed: _____

Meditation is essentially training our attention so that we can be more aware— not only of our own inner workings but also of what's happening around us in the here & now.   Sharon Salzberg

Prompt #1: Today I have spent my time thinking about ____

and these thoughts have made me feel _____

_____

_____

_____

Prompt #2: Today I choose to be mindful when I _____

_____ ,

and this is what I noticed during this time of attentiveness

and present moment awareness: _____

_____

_____

_____

Prompt #3: Today during meditation, I contemplate the essential value and importance of every person and recognize the interdependence of all living beings. I am no more or less important than anyone, even though my mind tries to tell me so. Here's what I noticed: _____

_____

_____

_____

_____

Knowledge does not mean mastering a great quantity of different information, but understanding the nature of mind. This knowledge can penetrate each one of our thoughts and illuminate each one of our perceptions.   Matthieu Ricard

Prompt #1: Today I have spent my time thinking about ____

_____

and these thoughts have made me feel _____

_____

_____

_____

Prompt #2: Today I choose to be mindful when I _____

_____ ,

and this is what I noticed during this time of attentiveness and present moment awareness: _____

_____

_____

_____

Prompt #3: Today during meditation, I rest in the space between thoughts. As I mentally reside in this space, it becomes more and more expansive. Here's what I noticed: _____

_____

_____

_____

_____

_____

_____

There's only one reason why you're not experiencing bliss at this present moment, and it's because you're thinking or focusing on what you don't have.... But, right now you have everything you need to be in bliss.

Anthony de Mello

Prompt #1: Today I have spent my time thinking about _____

_____

and these thoughts have made me feel _____

_____

_____

_____

Prompt #2: Today I choose to be mindful when I _____

_____ ,

and this is what I noticed during this time of attentiveness and present moment awareness: _____

_____

_____

_____

Prompt #3: Today during meditation, I acknowledge my accomplishment of practicing 90 days of meditation. I don't judge the quality of my meditations but simply become aware of my commitment and the various experiences I encountered. I feel at peace. Here's what I noticed: _____

_____

_____

_____

_____

_____

Final Thoughts
on Mindfulness Journaling

Congratulations on completing *The 90-Day Mindfulness Journal.*

You have dedicated the last 90 days to being more mindful in your daily life and improving your mindfulness efforts through daily meditation. Even if you journaled about your experiences for just a few minutes a day, you have not only increased your ability to be more present but also established a habit that will serve you for a lifetime.

Embracing mindfulness can have a transformative effect on your entire life. As we discussed, the mindfulness practice:

- Reduces rumination and overthinking.
- Decreases stress by decreasing the levels of the stress hormone cortisol.
- Improves memory, concentration, and performance.
- Helps maintain emotional stability. Improves relationship happiness.
- Reduces symptoms of anxiety and depression.
- Improves sleep.
- Protects against mental illness.
- Provides pain relief.

After journaling about mindfulness over the last 90 days, you've likely experienced several of these benefits. Not only will mindfulness practices improve your life, they will also have a spillover effect on everyone around you, as you will be a more focused, attentive, and contented person.

We encourage you to review this journal frequently and revisit some of the activities and meditations that you practiced over the last three months. We hope you will continue your meditation and mindfulness practices. But even if you don't practice daily, you will still enjoy many benefits from being more present and engaged in daily life.

Finally, we would love to hear about your experience with this journal, and the prompts you found most useful. If you'd like to share your thoughts, feel free to email us at sjscott@developgoodhabits.com or support@barriedavenport.com.

Thank you for investing your time and money in *The 90-Day Mindfulness Journal.*

We hope you enjoyed the journey!

Barrie Davenport & Steve "S.J" Scott

Works
Cited

[1] https://www.developgoodhabits.com/mindfulness-journal

[2] https://news.harvard.edu/gazette/story/2018/04/harvard-researchers-study-how-mindfulness-may-change-the-brain-in-depressed-patients/

[3] https://rd.springer.com/article/10.1007/s10608-007-9119-0

[4] http://www.mindfulschools.org/about-mindfulness/research/

[5] http://www.massgeneral.org/news/pressrelease.aspx?id=1329

[6] http://link.springer.com/article/10.1007/s11031-007-9076-7

[7] http://www.sciencedirect.com/science/article/pii/S1053810008001967

[8] http://mindfulnessmalta.com/user_files/2/mindfulness-and-relationships.pdf

[9] https://blogs.scientificamerican.com/guest-blog/what-does-mindfulness-meditation-do-to-your-brain/

[10] http://jamanetwork.com/journals/jamainternalmedicine/fullarticle/2110998

[11] https://www.sciencedaily.com/releases/2010/08/100816155000.htm

[12] https://nccih.nih.gov/research/blog/mindfulness-meditation-pain

[13] https://www.developgoodhabits.com/effortless-journaling

[14] https://lifehacker.com/281626/jerry-seinfelds-productivity-secret

Notes

Notes

_____

_____

_____

_____

_____

_____

_____

_____

_____

_____

_____

_____

_____

_____

_____

_____

_____

_____

_____

_____

_____

Notes

_____

_____

_____

_____

_____

_____

_____

_____

_____

_____

_____

_____

_____

_____

_____

_____

_____

_____

_____

_____

_____

Notes

Notes